AESOP'S FABLES

FOR MODERN READERS

Illustrated by Eric Carle

PETER PAUPER PRESS
Mount Vernon, New York

AESOP'S FABLES

FOR MODERN READERS

AESOP'S FABLES

THE GOAT AND THE WOLF

A Wolf chased a Goat, and the Goat jumped up on a high rock to escape. Then the Wolf lay down at the bottom of the rock, waiting for the Goat to come down. After three long days and nights of waiting, the Wolf said in a loud voice: I am hungry; I am going off to get some food! The Goat heard the Wolf say this, saw him go away into the forest, and jumped down from the rock. The first thing the Goat then did was to go to a brook which ran nearby, for he was terribly thirsty. As he was drinking, he saw his reflection in the water, and said: What magnificent legs I have! What a wonderful beard! And such horns! Just let that Wolf come back again, and I'll show him who is the better man! Just then, with a shout of laughter, the Wolf ran from the bushes where he had been hiding, and killed the Goat.

☞ It is better to use your head than to admire your whiskers.

THE FROG AND THE OX

A great Ox, grazing in a swamp, put down his foot on a family of young Frogs, and crushed most of them to death. One escaped, and ran off to his mother with the terrible news. Mother, he said, you never saw such a big beast as the beast that did it! Big? said the foolish old Mother Frog. She puffed herself to twice her size, and said, Was it as big as this? Oh, much bigger, said the little Frog. She puffed herself some more, and said: As big as this? Oh no, Mother, much, much bigger. So she puffed again, and puffed so very hard that suddenly with a great POP! she burst into little pieces.

☞ Small men can destroy themselves by striving to be bigger than they are.

THE SICK CROW

An old Crow was afraid he was dying, so he said to his children: Go out and pray to the gods that I may recover. Ah, Father, said the young Crows: To which of the gods can we pray? for you have spent your lifetime robbing the altars of them all, and taught us to do the same.

☞ A deathbed repentance is poor amends for a bad life.

THE ROOSTER AND THE EAGLE

Two young Roosters were fighting fiercely over a worm. Finally one of the Roosters was badly beaten and covered with wounds, so he ran away and hid in the hen-house. The conqueror, proud of his victory, flew to the top of the hen-house to tell the world about it. But an Eagle had been sailing around above the hen-house, waiting for a chance to catch himself some dinner; and no sooner did the Rooster start to crow, than the waiting Eagle swooped down, and carried him away.

☞ Don't crow in fast company.

THE TRAVELERS AND
THE PLANE-TREE

One hot day in summer, some travelers, over-heated by the noonday sun, saw a fine Plane-tree and made straight for it, so they might rest under its shade. As they lay looking up towards the tree, they said to each other, What a useless tree to man this barren Plane-tree is! But the Plane-tree answered them: Ungrateful creatures! At the very moment that you are enjoying the benefit of shade from me, you complain that I am good for nothing.

☞ Ingratitude is often blind.

THE HORSE AND THE STAG

In the old days the Horse had a whole meadow to himself, but once a Stag came and trampled up his pasture-ground. So the Horse went to a Man, and asked him to help get his revenge. Yes, said the Man; Just let me put this piece of metal in your mouth, and this leather thing on your back, and we will go after the Stag together. The Horse agreed, and the Man mounted and they went a-hunting, but after they had killed the Stag the Man kept the Horse as his slave.

☞ Revenge is not worth the loss of liberty.

THE CROW AND THE PITCHER

A crow was dying of thirst, and could find no brook or pond. At last he came to a hut, and outside the hut was a pitcher with water. But when he tried to drink the water, he couldn't reach down far enough. Then he tried to break the pitcher, but he wasn't strong enough. Finally he picked up small stones, one by one, and dropped them into the pitcher. At last the water rose high enough for him to reach, and he could quench his thirst.

☞ Necessity is the mother of invention.

9

THE FOX AND THE GRAPES

One day a hungry Fox stole into a farmer's yard where there were many bunches of grapes, ripe and juicy, hanging on a trellis. The Fox couldn't reach the grapes to eat them, so he jumped for the lowest bunch. As luck would have it, the grapes were just out of reach. He jumped, and jumped, and jumped again. But it was no use, and when he was tired from jumping he slunk away, saying: Who wants them anyway? I am sure the grapes are sour!

☞ Don't belittle good things because they are out of your reach.

THE DONKEY, THE FOX AND LION

A Donkey and a Fox made a hunting alliance, and went out together to look for game. The Fox was out in front, when he came upon a Lion, who was also hunting. The Fox, seeing his own danger, called softly to the Lion: King Lion, I have a Donkey here that you can have; I will lead you to him, if you will let me go. The Lion agreed; but no sooner had he killed the Donkey, than he turned on the Fox, and killed him too.

☞ Those who deal with traitors are not to be trusted.

THE TORTOISE AND THE EAGLE

A Tortoise was not satisfied with living in a little pond, when he saw his friends the birds flying where they pleased. He thought that he could learn to fly too, and asked the Eagle to take him up so he could learn. The Eagle told him he was mad; but the Tortoise begged and bothered him, and assured him he could fly. Finally the Eagle agreed, and carried the Tortoise high in the air. Are you high enough now? said the Eagle, looking back at his vain friend, the Tortoise. But the Tortoise, although frightened to death, opened his mouth to boast that he wanted to go higher, and thus lost his hold on the Eagle, and fell down, down, down, to his death.

☞ Pride cometh before a fall.

THE MOUNTAIN IN LABOR

Once a great Mountain was rumbling and groaning, and people came from far and wide to watch. It was said that the Mountain was going to give birth. Some said it would produce a Hill; some said an Ocean; some said a monstrous Animal. But after all the rumbling, groaning and shaking, the Mountain labored, and brought forth a Mouse!

☞ Great promises are not great deeds.

THE WIND AND THE SUN

The Wind and the Sun once had an argument as to which was the stronger. They looked down on the earth, and saw a traveler walking along the road, and decided to try their strength on him. The Wind had the first trial: he blew and blew with all his might, and as cold as he could. But the harder he blew, and the colder the wind, the tighter the traveler held his coat about him. When the Wind finally gave up, the Sun began to try. The Sun warmed the air, calmed the wind, and shone hotter and hotter upon the traveler, who first loosened his coat, and finally had to take it off his back entirely; and so the Sun won the contest.

☞ Persuasion is often a stronger power than mere force.

THE BOY AND THE NUTS

A Boy put his hand into a pitcher, which was half full of Nuts, and grasped just as many of them as his fingers could hold. But when he tried to take them out, his hand caught in the narrow neck, and he began to cry. At this, his father said: Foolish Boy! Take only half as much at one time:

☞ Greed defeats itself.

THE TREES AND THE AXE

A Woodcutter came into the forest one day to demand of the Trees that they give him a handle for his axe. It seemed a small demand for so great an enemy, and it was decided that the Woodcutter might have his way. But all the great trees refused to let themselves be sacrificed for the purpose; until finally the plain poor little Ash was told to give itself up for the handle. No sooner had the Woodman fitted his Ash handle, then he began to lay about him on all sides, and one after another of the great trees fell. Then the Oak shook its head and said to the Cedar: If we had not sacrificed our little neighbor, we would still be safe for ages to come.

☞ Stand together, or fall separately.

THE FLIES AND THE HONEY-POT

A Pot of Honey was upset in a Grocer's shop, and a swarm of Flies came to lap it up. It was so delicious that the Flies waded in deeper and deeper, until they found themselves caught in the Honey, and could not get away. What fools we are, said the Flies then, To lose our lives for a moment's pleasure!

☞ Do not let enjoyment lead you into danger.

THE THREE TRADESMEN

At one time an ancient city was afraid that it would be besieged by an enemy, so the elders of the town called a meeting to decide what kind of fortifications should be built. A Bricklayer stood up and said: There is nothing like brick! A Carpenter stood up and said: There is nothing like wood! A Tanner stood up and said: There is nothing like leather! Then a wise old farmer stood up and said: I do not want to spoil these gentlemen's business, but good old Mother Earth can still stop arrows; and if we use her, every man, woman, child and beast in this city can go to work for our mutual good.

☞ Profits and patriotism do not mix.

THE FROGS WHO ASKED FOR A KING

Once upon a time the Frogs decided that instead of everyone going about his life as he pleased, there ought to be a regular King and government. So with much croaking, they sent an ambassador to Jupiter. Mighty Jupiter, he cried, send us a king who will rule over us and keep us in order. Jupiter laughed, and threw down from heaven a huge Log which fell into the swamp with a great splash. The Frogs were frightened, and all rushed to the bank to look at the horrible monster; but after a time, seeing that it did not move, one of the boldest ventured out towards the Log, and even dared to touch it. Still it did not move. Then the greatest hero of the Frogs jumped upon the Log and danced up and down, whereupon all the Frogs came and did the same. Then for some time the Frogs went about their lives every day as before, without taking the slightest notice of King Log in their midst. But this did not suit them, so they sent another ambassador to Jupiter, and said: We want a real king; one that will really rule over us. This made Jupiter so angry that he sent them a Stork who ate two Frogs at every meal.

☞ Better no ruler than a hungry one.

THE EAGLE AND THE ARROW

A Hunter took aim with his Arrow at an Eagle, and the Arrow sped true to the mark, and struck the Eagle in the heart. The noble bird fell to the ground, and as he fell, he saw that the Arrow was winged with some of his own feathers. Ah, said the dying Eagle,

☞ How much sharper are the wounds of our own making.

THE HARE AND THE HOUND

A Hound having startled a Hare from a bush, chased her for some distance, but the Hare had the best of it, and got off. A Goatherd who was coming by jeered at the Hound, saying that the Hare was the better runner of the two. You forget, replied the Hound,

☞ It is one thing to be running for your dinner, and another for your life.

THE TWO WALLETS

Every man carries two wallets, one before and one behind, and both full of faults. But the one behind is full of his own. Thus it happens that men are blind to their own faults, but never lose sight of their neighbors'.

☞ Know thyself!

THE WOLF AND THE LAMB

A Wolf was drinking from a brook, when he saw a young Lamb in the water a little way below him. He ran up to her and shouted, Villain, how dare you muddy the water I am drinking? To this the Lamb replied humbly, I do not think I muddied your water, since the water was flowing from you to me, not from me to you. Maybe so! shouted the Wolf, But you called me many bad names a year ago! Oh Sir, said the Lamb, I was not born a year ago! Well, growled the Wolf, If it wasn't you, it was your Father — but there's no use trying to argue me out of my supper! And he leaped at the poor Lamb and ate her up.

☞ A villain may pause to look for excuses, but lack of excuses never stops him.

THE SHEPHERD AND THE WOLF

One day a Shepherd-boy was tired of sitting with his flock and doing nothing, so just for excitement he cried out at the top of his voice: Wolf! Wolf! The men from the village came running with axes, poles and rocks to attack the Wolf; but the Shepherd-boy laughed, and said it was just a joke. A week or two later he tried his joke again, and again the entire village turned out, only to be laughed at. But some time later the Wolf really did come, and the boy screamed and screamed, but nobody in the village paid any attention, and all his sheep were killed.

☞ Proven liars will not be believed even when they tell the truth.

THE GOAT AND THE VINE

A Wild Goat who was being chased by some hunters hid himself among the branches of a Vine. The Hunters passed by him without seeing him, but as soon as they had gone, he began to eat the thick branches that were covering him. Hearing the rustle of leaves, one of the hunters turned around, saw the head of the Goat as he pulled at the Vine, and shot the foolish animal after all.

☞ Do not destroy your protectors.

THE LION AND HIS THREE COUNCILLORS

The Lion called the Donkey to ask her if his breath smelled; she said: Yes! so he bit off her head for a fool. Then he called the Sheep, and asked him; the Sheep said: No! so he tore him to pieces for a flatterer. At last he called the Fox, and asked him. The Fox said, looking at the remains of the Donkey and the Sheep: I am sorry, your Majesty, but I have a bad cold, and cannot smell a thing!

☞ The wise man keeps silence in the reign of a tyrant.

THE DONKEY IN OFFICE

One day a Donkey was loaned by his master to the priest, to carry a religious image in a procession. As the Donkey marched through the town, he saw all the people bowing in reverence; and this made him so proud — for he thought they were bowing to him — that he decided he would not be driven any more. But the minute he stopped, his driver whipped him on again, saying: You silly Donkey, it is not you all the people are bowing to, but the sacred image which you are carrying.

☞ Fools take to themselves the respect that is shown to their office.

THE OAK AND THE REED

There was once a great Oak, which was very proud and stiff, and would not bow when the wind blew. And at his foot grew a Reed. One day the Oak said to the Reed: Why do you bow to every breeze? And the Reed said: Because I am not great and strong like you. To this the Oak replied: True, my poor friend, I am the strongest tree in the forest, while you are only a little piece of grass! But that night a great storm howled through the forest and while the Reed merely bent low as the wind blew over him, the great Oak stood stiffly in his pride, until at a sudden gust, he cracked in two.

☞ The proud shall be brought low, and the meek shall inherit the earth.

THE FOX WITHOUT A TAIL

A Fox was caught by his tail in a trap, and was glad enough to lose the tail in order to get away. But when he got back near his own forest neighborhood, he began to worry about what his neighbors would say to him. To make the best of a bad matter, he called a meeting of all the Foxes, and when they were gathered he spoke as follows: My friends, you have no idea how wonderful it is to have no tail. I would not have believed it if I hadn't tried it first myself. I feel *so* light, I can run so fast, that I am quite proud of myself. And of course a big tail is such an ugly and inconvenient thing! I wonder that we Foxes have put up with such things so long! I therefore propose, that from this day forward, all Foxes cut off their tails! There was some willingness to follow this plan, until an old wily Fox came forward. I wonder, said he, Why you never thought of cutting off our tails before you lost your own?

☞ Think twice when a beggar tells you to throw away your gold.

THE ANT AND THE GRASSHOPPER

One cold day in Winter an Ant was dragging out some corn which he had buried in the Summer. A Grasshopper, who was nearly starving, begged the Ant for only a small bit of corn, to save his life. What were you doing all last Summer? asked the Ant. Oh said the Grasshopper, I was very busy all Summer long, singing. Well, said the Ant, as he closed up his storehouse and walked off with the corn, Since you could sing all Summer, you can dance all Winter.

☞ Save in Summer: have in Winter.

THE DONKEY AND THE SALT

A merchant once loaded his Donkey with some bags of salt, and was driving her to town, when she slipped and fell into the water as they were crossing a plank over a small stream. The Donkey swam to shore, but the salt was all dissolved and streamed out of the bags, so that the Donkey had a light burden the rest of the way. The next day, again carrying salt, the Donkey managed to slip at the same spot, with the same result. Then the merchant decided to cure the Donkey of her habit, and the next day loaded her down with a great pile of Sponges. The foolish Donkey slipped again, but this time she could hardly drag herself out of the water with the soaking Sponges, and staggered into town under a tremendous load.

☞ Fools always play the same trick once too often.

THE HORSE AND THE GROOM

A Groom used to steal a Horse's corn and yet was very busy in grooming and currying him all the day long. Said the Horse:

☞ If you really wish me to look well, worry less about my skin, and more about my stomach.

THE OLD HOUND

An old Hound, who had been a fine hunter in his youth, one day was out with his master in the forest. They saw a wild Boar, and the Hound ran after him. He caught the Boar, but the Boar was young and strong, and after a struggle got away. Then the Hound's master came up, and was about to beat him. But the Hound said: Master, remember what I was in the old days, and the hunting I did for you then; and do not beat me for my weakness now.

☞ The old should be pitied, not punished, for their weakness.

THE WOLF AND THE SKULL

A Wolf, going through the forest, found the skull of a man. He turned it over and over with his paw, but the Skull said nothing and did nothing. Ah, said the Wolf: In times gone by, when you were a man, you would have had something to say; in those days you were fat and handsome, and you could laugh and sing, and eat, and drink, and be merry; but now you are only a silent hollow shell, and are good for nothing.

☞ Health and merriment soon disappear; only the works of man live on.

THE LION AND THE MOUSE

The Mouse went into a Lion's cave by mistake, and before he knew what he was doing, he ran over the nose of the sleeping Lion. The Lion reached out his paw and caught the Mouse, and was about to eat him when the Mouse said: Forgive me, King of Beasts, I did not know where I was. I should never have been so proud as to come into this cave if I had known it was yours. The Lion smiled at the poor frightened little Mouse, and let him go. Not long after this, the Lion fell into a rope net left for him by some hunters, and his roars filled the forest. The Mouse recognized the voice and ran to see if he could help him. He set to work nibbling the ropes, and soon the Lion was free.

☞ No one is so poor and powerless that he cannot return a good deed.

THE BEES AND THE DRONES

The Bees had built their comb in a hollow tree, but some Drones took possession of it and claimed it for their own. The case was brought before the wise old Wasp, who agreed that it was a difficult matter to decide. The only way to be sure who was the owner, he said, was for each party to build a new comb, and whoever made a comb most like the one in dispute, was the real owner. The Bees agreed, but the Drones said No. Then the wise Wasp said: It is clear now who made the comb, and who cannot make it. It belongs to the Bees.

☞ Honesty never fears a trial.

THE FOX AND THE ROOSTER

There was a Rooster in a little village who was very proud of his loud crowing. One day a crafty Fox came up to him and said: I hear you have a beautiful voice. On hearing this, the Rooster dug his claws in the earth, shut his eyes, and began to crow as loud as he could. The minute the Fox saw his eyes were closed, he seized him and carried him away. The people of the village shouted, and the Rooster said: Sir Fox, listen to the people of the town! They say that I am their Rooster, and you cannot take me away. Why don't you tell them that I am your Rooster now? So the Fox shouted: He is my Rooster now! — but the moment the Fox's mouth was opened, the Rooster got away again.

☞ Too much vanity brings trouble; too much careless talk brings loss.

THE SERPENT AND THE FILE

A Serpent crawled into a blacksmith's shop for something to eat. The best he could find was a File, so he tried to bite into it. But the File said: Leave me alone, fool! What chance have you against me, who can bite into the hardest steel?

☞ Test your meat before you eat.

THE WOLF IN SHEEP'S CLOTHING

Once a Wolf, who had trouble catching sheep, decided to disguise himself. So he found the skin of a sheep, and covered himself with it, and then mingled with the flock. By leading off young lambs one at a time when the Shepherd was not looking, the Wolf managed to feed himself well every day; but one afternoon, the Shepherd wanted to prepare a feast for his family and looked for the biggest animal in the flock. His eye fell on the Wolf in Sheep's clothing, and he killed him on the spot.

☞ Every deceit has its dangers.

THE FARMER AND THE DOGS

One winter the snow was so deep for weeks on end that a Farmer could not get outside his house and barn. Unable to get food from outside, he ate his own sheep; and when they were gone, had to eat his own goats. Still the snow held, and the Farmer killed one of his oxen. At this the Dogs said to one another, Let us be off while we can; he has kept us for the last only because he does not care for our meat.

☞ When your neighor's house is on fire, look to your own.

THE HOUSE-DOG AND THE WOLF

One night a hungry Wolf and a fat House-Dog met while roaming through the woods. My, how fat and nice you look, said the Wolf. You must get lots of good things to eat. As for me, I can hardly keep from starving. Well, said the Dog, If you want to help guard the Master's house with me, you'll get the same food I do. Fine, said the Wolf, I'm with you! But just as they were starting off home, the Wolf said: What is that thing around your neck? My collar, said the Dog. What is it for? asked the Wolf. Oh, they chain me up by it during the day, said the Dog. Goodbye, said the Wolf, I think I'll keep to my present life.

☞ Better a bone and liberty then plenty and a chain.

THE CRAB AND HER MOTHER

Said an old Crab to a young one, Why do you walk so crooked, child? walk straight! Mother, said the young Crab, Show me the way, will you? and when I see you walking straight, I will try to do the same.

☞ Practice what you preach.

THE BIRDS, THE BEASTS AND THE BAT

Once upon a time there was a great war between the Birds and the Beasts. For a long time neither side seemed to be winning, and the Bat, who was half a Bird and half a Beast, remained neutral. Finally, it looked as though the Beasts would win, and the Bat joined their army; but the Birds rallied, and finally won. When the winning army was being reviewed by the General, there was the Bat with the other Birds. Get back to your friends the Beasts, shouted the General. But the Beasts chased the Bat too, and from that day forward he has not dared to show his face except at night.

☞ Both sides despise a traitor.

THE LARK AND THE FARMER

There was a brood of young Larks in a field of grain; and as the grain was getting ripe the Mother Lark kept her eye out for the reapers. One day the Farmer came to the field, and said aloud: The grain is ripe, I must call in the neighbors to help me reap! OhMother, said the baby Larks, Let us fly away! No hurry, said the Mother: He will have to wait for his neighbors. The next day the Farmer came again, and said: The grain is fully ripe, I cannot wait for my neighbors; I must call in my relatives to help me. At this, all the baby Larks again wanted to fly away, but again the Mother Lark said: He will have to wait for his relatives. The next day the Farmer was desperate. Said he, I can't wait for my relatives: I will have to go to town and hire some laborers myself! At this the mother Lark said, All right, children, we really will have to move now; for

☞ When a man takes his own business upon himself and doesn't wait for others' help, he gets things done!

THE STAG AT THE POOL

One summer day a Stag came to a pool to drink, and saw himself reflected in the water. How beautiful and strong my antlers are, he said: But what a pity that my legs are so thin and ugly! Just then he heard the baying of hounds. The legs he had been complaining of carried him swiftly away from the hunters; but just as he thought he was safe, his beautiful horns caught themselves in the thicket, and before he could get them free the dogs were upon him.

☞ Usefulness is better than beauty.

THE HORSE AND THE DONKEY

A Traveler with a Donkey and a Horse, who
carried merchandise from town to town, was
in the habit of letting the Donkey carry all
the load. One hot day the Donkey was feeling
very weak and sick, and begged the Horse to
carry some of the load; for, said she, If I have
to carry all of it today I am going to collapse
for good; but if you will take part of it, I will
soon get well again and be able to carry it all.
But the Horse was proud and stubborn, and
said he didn't want to be bothered with the
complainings of a Donkey. The Donkey jog-

ged on in silence; but soon, what with the great heat and the heavy load, she fell down and died. At this, the master fastened the whole load on the Horse, and made him carry the dead Donkey besides, as far as the next tannery.

☞ An unwilling partner is his own undoing.

THE WOLF AND THE SHEPHERD

A crafty Wolf had for a long time hung about a flock of sheep and done them no harm. He pretended that he was reformed, and acted like a sheep-dog. After a while the Shepherd, who had begun by fearing him, looked upon him as a helper; and one day even went into town, thinking that the Wolf would guard the flock against any danger. But of course this was just the opportunity the Wolf had been waiting for, and while the Shepherd was away, the entire flock was killed.

☞ Beware of villains who act like friends.

THE AILING FOX

An old Lion, who was no longer quick enough to catch for himself all the food he needed in his usual way, sent out word that he was dying, and would appreciate a last visit from all his subjects. So one by one they came in sorrow to say a last goodbye to him, and one by one he ate them up. Finally the Fox arrived to pay his call, but being a cautious beast he stayed in the doorway, and from there he asked after his Majesty's health. Ah! my dearest friend, said the Lion, Is it you at last? Won't you come to me and speak a word of consolation in your poor King's ear, who has so short a time to live? Bless you, said the Fox, I would gladly do so, except I fear your sickness is catching, for look at all these footsteps leading in, and not a one going out!

☞ Don't trust the tyrant who asks for pity.

THE KID AND THE WOLF

One day a Kid that had strayed away from her flock was chased by a Wolf. She saw that she could not get away, so she turned to the Wolf and said: I can see that I am done for; but since my life is to be so short, pray permit me to make it a merry one. If you will only play on your pipes for me, I will dance, and so die happy. The Wolf agreed, and played on his pipes; but no sooner did he start to play, than the Shepherd's dog, hearing the strange music, came running to see, and soon chased him away.

☞ He who contracts to play the fool, must expect to be deceived.

THE MONKEY AND THE DOLPHIN

A sailor in ancient Greece had a Monkey on board ship as his pet. One day, as the ship neared Athens, there was a violent storm, the ship began to sink, and everyone on board jumped into the water. The Monkey, too, was swimming landward as well as she could, when a Dolphin came up to the surface, and taking the Monkey for a man, let her climb on his back so that he could carry her to the shore. As they came near Piraeus, the harbor of Athens, the Dolphin asked:

Are you a citizen of Athens? The Monkey said that she was. Then you know Piraeus? asked the Dolphin. Know Piraeus! said the ignorant Monkey, Why, he is one of my best friends! Disgusted at having taken on a lying passenger, the Dolphin plunged beneath the surface again, leaving the Monkey to sink or swim for herself.

☞ Be honest with your friends or you will lose them.

THE VAIN JACKDAW

The Jackdaw, a vain, foolish, ugly bird, picked up a lot of Peacock feathers, stuck them among his own, and passing by his friends with beak in air, he marched among the proud Peacocks as though he were one of them. The Peacocks saw that he was only a Jackdaw, pulled off his fancy feathers, and pecked him back to his own side of the yard. There he went to his own friends for comfort, but they remembered that he had walked past without noticing them before, and in revenge pecked at him worse than the Peacocks.

☞ Avoid false feathers: your betters will not accept you, and your equals will resent you.

THE TWO POTS

Two Pots, one of earthenware, the other of brass, were carried down a river together in a flood. The Brass Pot urged the Earthen Pot to keep by his side, for their mutual protection. Thank you for your offer, said the Earthen Pot, But that is just what I am afraid of; if you will only keep at a distance, I may float down in safety; but should we touch, I am sure to suffer.

☞ Avoid powerful neighbors, for in a collision, the weakest goes down.

THE HEN AND THE CAT

A sly Cat, who had caught more than one chick in her day, hearing that a Hen was laid up sick in her nest, paid her a visit of sympathy. She crept up to the nest and said softly: How are you, my dear friend? what can I do for you? what are you in want of? only tell me, if there is anything that I can bring you. But you must keep up your spirits, and don't be alarmed. Thank you, said the Hen; But if you will be good enough to leave me alone, and ask your sisters to do likewise, I am sure I will recover my good health.

☞ The good wishes of an enemy make the wise man nervous.

THE HARE AND THE TORTOISE

One warm afternoon a Hare was making fun of the Tortoise because he was so slow. The Tortoise laughed, and said he would beat the Hare any time he wanted. Come on then, said the Hare, and I'll show you what kind of runner I am! They decided to race to the forest, a mile or so away. The Tortoise started off at once, at his steady pace; but the Hare said boastfully, I think I'll take a little nap first, I've plenty of time to spare. But when the Hare woke up, the sun was setting in the west, and though he raced to the edge of the forest as fast as he could go, he found the Tortoise there before him.

☞ Slow and steady wins many a race.

THE DOG IN THE MANGER

A Dog made his bed in the manger one afternoon, and when the horses came in after a hard day's work, he barked and snarled at them. Every time they tried to take some of their hay the Dog chased them away, until finally the oldest and wisest of them said to the Dog: Come here and I'll give you some good advice:

☞ Do not begrudge to others what you cannot enjoy yourself.

THE WOLVES AND THE SHEEP

One day the Wolves sent an ambassador to the Sheep, saying that they desired peace between them from that time forward. Why on earth, said the ambassador, Should we always be waging war against each other? Those wicked Dogs are the real cause of all the trouble, because they are always barking at us and provoking us to battle. Send them away, and you will see that there will always be peace and friendship between us. The silly Sheep did as they were told, but as soon as the Dogs were gone, the Wolves raided the flock whenever they wished.

☞ Don't dismiss your friends at the first criticism from your enemies.

THE FAWN AND THE MOTHER

A Fawn one day said to her mother: Mother, you are bigger than a dog, and swifter and better winded, and you have horns to defend yourself; how is it that you are so afraid of the hounds? The mother smiled and said, All this, my child, is true; but no sooner do I hear a dog bark, than, somehow or other, my heels take me off as fast as they can carry me.

☞ You cannot argue a coward into courage.

THE FOX AND THE CROW

A Fox once saw a Crow fly off from a kitchen window with a piece of cheese in her beak, and settle in a tree to eat the delicacy. So the Fox walked up to the foot of the tree. Crow, he cried, How beautiful you are looking to-day; how glossy your feathers are, how bright your eyes; I am sure your voice, too, is more lovely than that of other birds! At this the vain Crow began to caw her very best, but the moment she opened her mouth the piece of cheese fell to the ground, and was snatched by the Fox. That will do, my foolish friend, said he, and he ran away. That was all I wanted, and in exchange I will give you a piece of advice you should never forget:

☞ Don't trust flatterers.

THE MICE AND THE WEASELS

The Mice and the Weasels had long been at war with each other, and the Mice had always lost the battles. So a great conference of the Mouse leaders was called to find the fault and propose a cure. After much argument, it was decided that the Mice were at

a disadvantage because they did not have regular officers, each in charge of a company or regiment. So the bravest of the Mice were appointed officers, and these officers, proud of their position, decided to affix horns to their heads as a sign of authority and in order to frighten the Weasels. After the next battle, when the Weasels defeated the Mice as usual, the horned officers ran away just like the other Mice. But while the others scurried into their holes, the officers stuck in the entrances because of their new horns, and they were all caught and eaten by the Weasels.

☞ There can be no distinction without danger.

THE ROOSTER AND THE DIAMOND

As a Rooster was scratching around in the straw of his barnyard, looking for worms, he came upon a brilliant diamond that someone had lost there. All the Hens fluttered around to see it, and admire it; but the Rooster went on with his scratching elsewhere. It's a fine thing for those who can use it, no doubt, he said, But as for me, I hope I can keep on finding corn and worms.

☞ The greatest jewel will not satisfy hunger.

THE LION AND THE DONKEY
OUT HUNTING

A Lion and a Donkey made an agreement to go hunting together. The Donkey went around to the back of a cave where there were many wild goats, while the Lion placed himself at the entrance. Then the Donkey brayed, kicked and made a mighty fuss, so that the goats all ran out, and were caught by the Lion. Didn't I make a wonderfully frightening noise? said the Donkey later to the Lion, as they feasted. Ah! yes indeed! said the Lion, and I would have been frightened too, if I hadn't known you were a complete Donkey.

☞ Boast before your betters and be laughed at for a fool.

THE WOLF AND THE GOAT

A Wolf, seeing a fat Goat feeding at the edge of a high cliff, begged her to come down lower, for fear, he said, that she might miss her footing and be hurt. And anyway, he added: The grass is really much sweeter and greener down here. To which the Goat replied: Is it to my dinner you invite me, or your own?

☞ When the villain smiles, he baits his trap.

THE BLACKSMITH AND HIS DOG

A Blacksmith once took in a Dog, who asked if he could have a home and make himself useful, promising to do all sorts of helpful things around the smithy. But while the Blacksmith hammered away at his metal, the Dog slept; and when he sat down to dinner, the Dog woke up and wagged his tail. You lazy cur! said the disgusted Blacksmith, tossing him a bone, You sleep through all the noise of the anvil but wake up at the first clatter of dishes.

☞ If you avoid your friend at work, do not join him at meals.

THE STAG IN THE OX-STALL

A hunted Stag, knowing that if he kept running he would soon be caught by the huntsmen, ran for a Farmer's barn near the edge of the wood. He came in the doorway, and hid himself under the straw in an empty stall. The Ox in the next stall said to him, You must be desperate indeed to come to the haunts of men; and the Stag answered, Only do not betray me, and I will get away after dark! The huntsmen came to the barn, but they did not see the Stag, and went ahead. Evening came on; the milkmaids milked the cows, but they did not see the Stag. The Farmers unharnessed the horses, and put away the wagons and tools, but they did not see the Stag. The Stag, now feeling himself safe, began to thank the Oxen for their silence, but they said, Wait, you are still in danger; for there is one man who sees everything. Just then the Master, having finished his supper, came in to see that all was well for the night. Prying and observing, he soon caught sight of the Stag's antlers in the straw, and that was the end of the Stag.

☞ No eye like the Master's.

THE COUNTRY MOUSE AND
THE CITY MOUSE

Once upon a time a Country Mouse invited his friend the City Mouse for a visit. The Country Mouse lived quite a plain life, but when his guest arrived from the city, he was most hospitable and generous to his old friend, and brought out all his savings of nuts, cheese-parings, bread and barley. He knew the City Mouse was used to fancier food, but he hoped that among all his store there would be something to please. The City Mouse ate a nibble here and a nibble there, and finally said: My dear fellow, this is all very healthy and good, no doubt, but really, your are wasting your life in this hole. A Mouse lives only once, you know, and if you don't see the gay life and eat the fine food of the city now, you may never get another chance. Why don't you come to town with me, and I'll give you a taste of real life? The Country Mouse was tempted, and they set off for town. Late at night they arrived at the great house where the City Mouse was living. The Country Mouse was shown all the fine furnishings, the silks and velvets; and then he was escorted to the dining room. There on the table were the remains of a banquet, and the City Mouse made his country cousin taste all the fine foods, and even the wine which was in the bottom of the glasses. The Country Mouse was very excited by all this grandeur, and had made up his mind to stay, when there was a burst of noise, and the people of the house rushed in from some late party. The frightened Mice scurried off the table and behind a drapery, but two dogs which had come in with the people barked at them there, and they had to run for the cellar. There the Country Mouse whispered goodbye to his friend, and said:

☞ Better to live on barley and be your own master, than to live on cream at the mercy of kings.

THE MICE IN COUNCIL

The Mice were desperate because of the Cat, who caught one or two of them every night. So they called a council, to decide how best to put an end to their troubles. Many plans were suggested and discarded; but at last a smart young Mouse spoke up and said: Why not put a bell on the Cat, so that we can hear her coming? Everyone thought that this was really a fine idea, and a vote was about to be taken, when a shrewd old Mouse, who had kept quiet up till then, remarked: This is a perfect solution, but I have one little question I should like to ask: Who is going to bell the Cat?

☞ It is one thing to make great plans; and another to carry them out.

THE THIRSTY PIGEON

A Pigeon was extremely thirsty, and had looked everywhere for water, but in vain. At last she saw a glass of water painted on an inn-sign; and without waiting to see if it was real, she swooped down and crashed into the signboard, breaking her wing. The inn-keeper took her in, and cured her wing; but she was a prisoner from that time on.

☞ Never let thirst betray your judgment.

THE GOOSE WITH THE GOLDEN EGGS

Long ago a Farmer had a magical Goose, that laid a golden egg every day. Naturally, this Goose was the wonder of the countryside, and all the other farmers envied her rich owner. But once he had a taste of the gold, this Farmer could not get enough of it. Anxious to get all of the gold supply at once, he killed the Goose one night — only to find that there was no gold inside at all.

☞ Always protect the source of your good fortune.

THE WIDOW AND THE HEN

A Widow had a plump Hen who laid an egg every day, without fail. The Widow thought to herself: If I give the Hen twice as much barley, she will lay twice as many eggs. So she fed the Hen twice a day. But after a few days, the Hen became so fat, that she stopped laying eggs at all.

☞ You can't bribe Nature.

THE SICK LION

A Lion had come to the end of his days and lay dying in his cave, gasping for breath. All the other animals came round him and drew nearer as he grew more and more helpless. Then they thought to themselves: Now is the time to pay off old grudges. So the Boar came up and drove at him with his tusks; then a Bull gored him. Still the Lion lay helpless before them, so the Donkey, feeling quite safe from danger, trotted up in his turn, and turning his tail to the Lion, kicked his heels into his face.

☞ This is twice as bad as death, said the old Lion, to have my helpless majesty insulted by a coward!

THE MILLER, HIS SON AND THE DONKEY

A Miller and his Son were taking their Donkey to market to sell him. They passed some laughing girls, who said to the boy: Silly, what is a Donkey good for? Why don't you ride on him? So the Miller told his Son to ride on the Donkey. They hadn't gone far along when they passed an old man, who grumbled: Look at that lazy boy! Letting his father walk while he rides! So the Miller got on the Donkey, and the Son walked. After a little way farther, they passed some women, who clacked: Lazy man! Riding in luxury while that poor boy trots along in the dust! So the Miller took his son up on the Donkey with him. As they got near town, a man saw them and shook his head: That poor little Donkey, he said, Carrying two big louts like you. You ought to be ashamed of yourselves! So the Miller and his Son got off the Donkey, and to prevent any further criticism they tied his legs together, got a long pole, and marched into town with the beast slung between them. As they crossed over the bridge the fishermen laughed at them for fools, the boy began to cry, the Donkey began to twist and kick, until the boy let go his end of the pole and the beast tumbled into the river.

☞ If you try to please everyone you will end by pleasing no one.

THE TRAVELERS AND THE BEAR

Two travelers were going through the forest together to a nearby town. They had agreed to help each other in case of danger; but suddenly they came upon a Bear, and one of the men, forgetting his companion, immediately started to climb a tree. The other saw he had no chance against the Bear if he fought alone, so he lay down on the ground and played dead. The Bear came up to him, and sniffed all around him. The Traveler knew that the Bear would not touch a dead body, so he held his breath; and after sniffing around the man's head again, the Bear finally went away. As soon as the Bear was out of sight the second man slid down from his tree and said laughing: What was it the Bear whispered to you? For I saw that he put his mouth close to your ear? Oh, said the other, He told me something I had learned already: he merely said:

☞ Beware of friends who leave you in the lurch.

THE CAT AND THE MICE

A wily old Cat, who had been having trouble catching Mice because she was now a bit slow, and because the Mice were getting too smart, thought up a scheme for fooling them. She hung herself up by the hind legs from a beam in the barn, and expected that the Mice would take her for a bag or an old coat. In came the Mice, as soon as all was dark; but at the first glance the leader said: Mm! Many a bag have I seen in my day but never a one with a Cat's head! And all the other Mice, even the baby Mice, laughed and laughed at the Cat until she could stay still no longer, but angrily started to untie herself. Then all of the Mice scampered safely away.

☞ If a Mouse can smell cheese, he can also smell trouble.

THE MISER AND THE THIEF

Once there was a Miser, who buried his bag of gold at the foot of a tree, and came back to look at it every day. One day a Thief watched the Miser dig in the earth, take out his bag and fondle it, and then put back the bag, and cover it with earth. That night the Thief took away the gold, and left in its place a bag of stones, which he carefully covered over as before. The next day the Miser went to fondle his gold as usual; and finding only stones, he raised such an outcry that all the neighbors came to hear his story. What did you do with all that gold? asked one of the neighbors. Why, nothing, said the Miser, I only used to come and look at it. Well, said the other, Come and look every day at the bag of stones, then; it will do you just as much good!

☞ Hoarded wealth is useless wealth.

THE FARMER AND HIS SONS

An old Farmer felt that he was dying, and wanted to be sure that his sons continued to take good care of the fields and crops as before. So calling them to his bedside, he said: I am dying. But before I go I must tell you: My fortune is in the fields where we grow our crops. The sons thought that their father had hidden gold in the fields, and as soon as the old man died, they set to work with spade, hoe and plough to find the buried treasure. They found no treasure, but by their search the fields were cultivated as never before, and the crops were so fine the sons were well rewarded for their digging.

☞ The good earth is a treasure for those who will dig in it.

THE FIR-TREE AND THE BRAMBLE

A Fir-tree was one day boasting of itself to a Bramble, and said: *You* are of no use at all; but how could barns and houses be built without me? Good sir, said the Bramble, When the woodmen come here with their axes and saws, what would you give to be a Bramble and not a Fir?

☞Humbleness in security is better than loftiness in danger.

THE COUNTRY MAID AND
THE MILK-JUG

A Country Maid was walking to market with a full Milk-jug on her shoulder; and as she walked, she said to herself: With the money for this milk, I will buy myself some setting eggs; I will raise the chicks from these eggs until they are big enough for market; and when I sell them, I will have enough money to buy myself a beautiful new green gown. With this green gown I will look so beautiful, that all the young men will want to court me. But I will act proud, and shrug my shoulders so . . . and down crashed the milk-jug into a hundred pieces!

☞ Don't count your chickens before they are hatched.

THE LIONESS AND HER CUB

Once there was great rivalry among the beasts, each one claiming to have the largest family. Finally the disputing beasts came to the Lioness, and said: Queen Lioness, how many children do you have at a birth? Only one! growled the Lioness. But that one is a Lion.

☞ Quality before quantity.

THE FOX AND THE STORK

One day the Fox invited the Stork to dinner, and for a joke had nothing served but some soup in a shallow dish. The Fox could easily lap up this soup, but the Stork could only wet the end of her long bill in it, and left the meal as hungry as when she came. I am so sorry, said the Fox, that the soup is not seasoned to your taste! Do not apologize, said the Stork, But I do hope you will return this visit, and come and dine with me soon. So another day the Fox visited the Stork; and when they were seated at table all they were served for dinner was in a long jar with a narrow mouth. From this the Stork could eat easily, but all the Fox could do was to lick the outside of the jar. Do not apologize for the dinner, said the Fox:

☞ One bad turn deserves another.

THE DOG, THE ROOSTER AND FOX

A Dog and a Rooster went traveling together. When night fell, they were in a forest, so the

Rooster flew up into the branches of a tree, while his friend slept below at the foot. At dawn the Rooster crowed, as he always did, and a Fox in that part of the forest came over to see if he couldn't make a meal of him. So he said to the Rooster very solemnly: You are a good bird, the best of creatures, to call us all to morning prayer. Come down, that we may pray together! But the Rooster was no fool, so he said, Go to the foot of the tree, and have the Sexton there ring the bell. Just as the Fox came to the foot of the tree, the Dog jumped out, and killed him.

☞ Those who lay traps must beware of being caught in them themselves.

THE FOX AND THE WOODMAN

A Fox that was being chased by the hounds, came to a Woodman, and begged him for a place to hide. The Woodman showed him his own hut, where the Fox hid behind the bed. The hunters soon came up, and asked the Woodman if he had seen the Fox. No, said the Woodman in a loud voice, but pointed with his hand toward the hut. But the hunters didn't take the hint, and rode off. As soon as they were out of sight, the Fox crept out and started off. Hollo, said the Woodman, Is this the way you treat your host, going off without a word? Ah, said the Fox, You are a pretty host! If your hands were as honest as your tongue, I should not go off without any thanks.

☞ Sometimes a wink is as good as a word.

THE HARES AND THE FROGS

The Hares were so frightened by the other beasts that they did not know where to go. All the other animals seemed to pursue them, so one day they decided to put an end to all their fears and troubles by drowning themselves in a lake nearby. But just as the crowd of Hares came running to the lake, all the Frogs, frightened in their turn by the Hares, scuttled off into the water. Truly, said the leader of the Hares, things are not so bad as they seem:

☞ There is always some one worse off than yourself.

THE THIEF AND THE DOG

Once there was a Thief who thought he was very clever. He used to boast to his friends that no lock could keep him out, and no dog could frighten him. One night he came to rob a Farmer's house; but the Dog saw him,

and started to bark. There, there! Good dog-
gie! said the Thief, and threw the Dog a fine
piece of meat. At this the faithful Dog barked
louder than ever, For, said he to the Thief:
I was suspicious of you at first, but now I
know you are up to no good whatsoever!

☞ Honeyed words and a bribe in hand pre-
cede some villainy.

THE FOX AND THE GOAT

A Fox had fallen into a well, and was won-
dering how he would ever get out again,
when along came a Goat. The Goat was
thirsty, and seeing the Fox in the well, he
asked if the water was good and plentiful.
Good! said the crafty Fox, This is the best
water I have ever tasted, and the more I
drink, the more comes in. At this the foolish
Goat jumped in beside the Fox, whereupon
the Fox scrambled onto the Goat's back, then
onto his horns, then up and out of the well.
Too bad, said the Fox to the Goat, with a
laugh, Too bad you haven't as much brains
as you have beard!

☞ Look well before you leap.

THE WOLF AND THE CRANE

A Wolf had a bone caught in his throat, and
ran through the forest in agony, begging

every animal he met to help him, and promising a handsome reward. The Crane, hearing of a reward, said she would help him. She put her long bill and neck down the Wolf's throat, and drew out the bone. Then she asked for her reward. At this the Wolf showed his teeth, and growled: Ungrateful creature! It is reward enough to put your head into a Wolf's jaws, and take it out again alive!

☞ Those who help others only for profit, must beware of helping evil men.

HERCULES AND THE WAGONER

A Farmer was driving his wagon carelessly along a muddy road, when the wheels sank into the soft clay, and the horses came to a standstill. Whipping and shouting at the horses did no good: the wagon would not budge. Then the Farmer climbed into the back of the wagon, and kneeled down to pray to Hercules. Good god Hercules, he cried, Help me now with your great strength! But Hercules looked down, and said: My good man, first put your own shoulder to the wheel:

☞ The gods help those who help themselves.

THE BUNDLE OF STICKS

A Farmer was worried because his Sons, instead of working together in peace and friendship, were always quarreling. So finally he said to them: Boys, go out into the field and gather me a bundle of sticks. After some argument, the two youngest were forced to get the sticks. The Farmer then tied the sticks into a bundle with strong cord, and said, Now, break this bundle! They tried; first one, then all together, but the sticks would not break. Now untie the bundle, and break the sticks separately, said the Farmer; and they did so without any trouble at all. Let this be a lesson to you, then said the Father, That you must stop your quarreling, and you must all work together,

☞ For in union there is strength.

THE SHEEP AND THE WOLF

A Sheep, standing on the roof of a barn, saw a Wolf passing below him. Ho there! you ugly Wolf! he called. Get home! We don't want your kind of trash around this farm! Coward, said the Wolf, Remember your words when we meet again in the pasture!

☞ Do not boast in the fort if you cannot fight in the field.